de-stress

de-stress

101 ways to relax

Jenny Sutcliffe

MQP

Published by MQ Publications Limited
12 The Ivories, 6-8 Northampton Street,
London N1 2HY
Tel: 020 7359 2244
Fax: 020 7359 1616
email: mail@mqpublications.com
website: www.mqpublications.com

Copyright © MQ Publications 2004
Text copyright © Jenny Sutcliffe 2004

Series Editor: Karen Ball, MQ Publications
Editorial Director: Ljiljana Baird, MQ Publications
Senior Designer: Victoria Bevan, MQ Publications
Design concept: Balley Design Associates
Photography: Stuart Boreham

ISBN 1-84072-587-7

Printed in France by *Partenaires-Livres*® (JL)

1 3 5 7 9 0 8 6 4 2

Caution
Aromatherapy oils should not be placed directly on the
skin and should always be diluted. Women who are
pregnant or hoping to become pregnant, or people
suffering from any medical condition, have circulatory
disease or diabetes should seek medical advice
before undertaking any of the recommendations in
this book.

This book is intended as an informational guide only
and is not to be used as a substitute for professional
medical care or treatment. Neither the author nor the
publisher can be held responsible for any damage,
injury, or otherwise resulting from the use of the
information in this book.

contents

Introduction

When our ancestors came across a saber-toothed tiger they had to react very quickly indeed. Adrenaline coursed through their bodies, blood pressure went up, breathing speeded up, and energy supplies were pumped to the muscles, preparing the body for fight or flight.

Today we still react to a perceived threat in the same way, though at different levels of intensity. But the trouble is that our ancestors' adrenaline was used up by their reaction to the threat, whereas we rarely experience any such release. As a result, many people in our high-pressure modern society are almost permanently physically and emotionally prepared for decisive action—which is never taken.

This state of constant preparedness is what we call stress. And it takes a heavy toll, both physically and mentally. It's not just that stress is linked to many physical and psychological disorders—it can mess up your life in other more subtle and insidious ways. Stress saps your energy, diminishes your chances of success, inhibits creativity, makes it almost impossible to think clearly, and can lead to depression and low self-esteem.

Va Va Voom De-Stress shows you how to reduce stress and not only reap the health benefits but also release your vital energies, so that you can regain control of your life—both at work and at home—lift your mood, and recapture your get-up-and-go. These 101 techniques will show you how to change your life. Get ready.

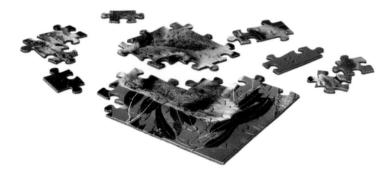

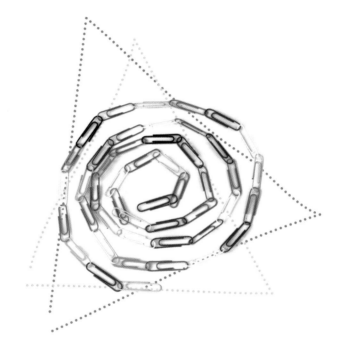

De-stress for work

Follow these tips for making the office
a better place to be and your working
life less of a headache.

1 Break for lunch

"Lunch is for wimps," said the masters of the universe. But look what happened to them.

The fact is that snatching a sandwich at your desk just increases your stress levels. It's important to take a lunch break—if only to get away from your desk, stretch out, relax, and get some fresh air. But what you eat is important, too. Chemicals in proteins are converted to neurotransmitters in the brain, which make you more alert. However, too much protein can make you twitchy rather than alert, so balance your protein intake with carbohydrates—these increase your brain levels of calming serotonin.

2 Stretch out

Sitting at a desk for long periods can cause physical stresses that lead to mental stress. The solution? Take five minutes out for a few stretches every hour.

Slump back in your chair, tilting your pelvis up, then sit up tall, arching your lower back and tilting your pelvis back. Next, spinal twists: fold your arms at shoulder height, cross one leg over the other and twist your upper body and head to right and left alternatively; change legs and repeat. Finally, circle your shoulders backward; then forward. Repeat each exercise five times—then you'll be able to think clearly and stay on the ball.

3 Make a to-do list

Do you ever get the feeling that there's just too much to do? Do you start one job and then get distracted by another? You probably become more and more stressed and never get anything done.

If this sounds like you, just take a deep breath, put the phone onto voice mail and stand back from your in-tray for a moment. Make a list of your tasks and prioritize them. Then force yourself to work through the list, sticking to each task until you've completed it. It's a guaranteed way to reduce stress and give yourself the satisfaction of a job well done.

4 Green peace

Most offices are reservoirs of germs and toxins: among others, benzene, formaldehyde, and trichloroethylene. At high levels, these can cause "sick building syndrome," and even in lower concentrations they can cause stress and ill-health.

But it couldn't be more simple to combat toxic vapors and relieve the stress they cause. A recent NASA study has shown that a few simple pot plants on your desk can work wonders. A bamboo palm (Chamaedorea seifrizii) and an English ivy (Hedera helix) will soak up benzene, formaldehyde, and trichloroethylene. And if you can run to it, an orchid (Dendrobium) deals with just about everything else.

5 Give it a squeeze

Your boss is putting you under pressure, your colleagues aren't cooperating, and your customers are making impossible demands—you're severely stressed. So what can you do?

You can't yell at your boss, curse your colleagues, and ignore your customers—obviously. But you can take out all your pent-up aggression and de-stress with a stress ball. Buy one from a health store or the Internet and squeeze it, knead it, pummel and pound it whenever things get on 'top of you. And for extra relaxation, take off your shoes and roll it under your feet for a quick reflexology massage. Alternatively, invest in a wooden foot roller to keep under your desk.

6 Hit the delete button

One of the downsides of the information age is e-mail overload. Many people spend ages going through junk e-mail and messages that don't concern them—in fact, it's a major cause of office stress.

So take the bull by the horns. Use your e-mail program's "message rules" to filter out unwanted e-mails and prioritize the ones you want into categories according to their importance—ask your system administrator for help if necessary. Don't respond to jokes or circulars—just delete them—and keep a private free e-mail account for all personal messages. Your stress levels will plummet.

7 Take five

Studies have shown that most people can only concentrate fully for about 50 minutes—after that, both output and efficiency fall. And that means that stress levels rise.

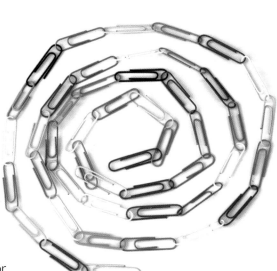

So in order to work with maximum efficiency and minimal stress, take time out for five minutes every hour. It doesn't matter what you do, just so long as it's mindless—make a snake with paper clips, for example. (Or you could take the opportunity to do some stretches or a de-stressing Pilates exercise.) But don't play solitaire on your computer—your eyes need a break, too.

 Clear the air

Scientists have known for some time that negative ions—airborne particles with a negative electrical charge—are good for health. They have the same bracing and invigorating effect as breathing in sea air or standing by a waterfall.

But it's only recently been realized that negative ions are especially important in the office. It's because the cathode ray tubes in VDUs produce a positive charge that sweeps up the negative ions. The result can be headaches, concentration problems, and difficulty with completing complex tasks—and women are more affected than men. The answer? Buy a desk ionizer and recharge your personal space.

9 Manage your meetings

It's always stressful when you have to take a meeting, but if you follow a few simple rules you'll keep stress at bay.

Have all the facts at your fingertips; don't waffle; assess reactions and adapt your presentation accordingly. Above all, appear confident, even if there are butterflies in your stomach.

10 Pilates de-stress

Pilates techniques don't just tone your body—they also relieve stress. This exercise, "Rolling Down the Wall," calms you, releases tension in your shoulders, and smoothes out your spine.

Stand tall with your back against a wall, your feet about eight inches out from it, your hands by your side, and your belly sucked in. Inhale and move your chin down toward your chest, unrolling your vertebrae one by one and letting you arms hang loosely. Breathe naturally, keep your belly in, and circle your arms five times in each direction. Finally, inhale, roll back up the wall and exhale.

11 Power nap

The National Sleep Foundation, based in Washington, D.C., says that our body temperature drops between two and four o'clock in the afternoon and we can feel sleepy. Ring a bell?

Their answer is to take a 15- to 20-minute power nap to restore mental alertness. Some employers now provide rooms in which staff can lay down a mat and take a quick nap. But don't overdo it—the NSF's research shows that napping for more than 20 minutes makes you more tired.

12 Learn to delegate

Do you take on too much? Do you find it difficult to trust other people to do their jobs properly? If so, you've cooked up a classic recipe for stress.

It's important to get back on an even keel, otherwise you won't do your own job properly—and that will create even more stress. Learn to trust colleagues and delegate tasks. That way they, not you, will be responsible for what they produce and you'll be able to concentrate on your own tasks. It's good management and a surefire stress reliever.

13 Look on the bright side

It's not always easy to look on the bright side of life, especially when you're stressed. But optimism reduces stress—and it can be learnt.

Psychologists recommend using the TSE view—it stands for Temporary, Specific, and External—to put negative events in perspective and reduce their stress potential. So, for example, when your boss criticizes your latest report, just think "T"—I'll correct the mistakes I made next time; "S"—it was basically OK but next time I'll work harder with the visuals; and "E"—she was having a bad day. That way you'll relieve stress and empower yourself for the future.

14 Calming sensations

What do lavender, cucumber, and green apples have in common? According to the Smell and Taste Treatment and Research Foundation, in Chicago, it's that their scents lull us into relaxation.

Try it out. Buy a sachet of lavender—or, better still, keep a vase of fresh lavender on your desk and let its rich, musky scent soothe your tension away. Alternatively, slice up a fresh, moist cucumber and either eat the slices or use them as a face pack. And, of course, you could always crunch into a crisp green apple—and keep the doctor away.

15 Kick the caffeine habit

Coffee tends to be a staple of office life. The trouble is that in fact caffeine—and sugar, too, if you take it—ends up reducing your energy levels. It boosts them for a short time, but then they fall below their starting point. (And if you're tempted to slip outside for a quick cigarette, you'll be disappointed to hear that the same is true of nicotine.)

Reduced energy levels mean increased stress. So give up coffee and cola drinks, and refresh yourself with fruit, water or a non-caffeine herbal drink instead. You'll feel more energized and less stressed.

16 De-clutter and de-stress

Are you one of those people whose desk is a mess but claims to know exactly where everything is? You don't always, do you? And just think of the time you waste when you try to find that vital document—with your stress levels rising as you search for it.

Turn over a new leaf, de-clutter, and de-stress. File all your papers, and be ruthless when deciding what to keep and what to throw away. Are you really going to look at that press cutting again? By the time you've finished, you'll feel like a new, stress-free person.

17 Time management

Office life makes a thousand and one calls on your time—
a meeting at 11, a report to finish by 3, and Accounts are
demanding your expenses forms. And unless you manage
your time properly, you'll not only become inefficient but
seriously stressed.

Time management is the answer, even on a limited scale.
Just spend the last ten minutes or so of each day planning
your next day. Give yourself time to prepare for meetings
and sort out any schedule clashes. Just knowing what
you're meant to be doing and taking control of your day
will significantly reduce your stress.

18 Under pressure

It's generally accepted that acupuncture is an effective pain reliever, but it's not so well known that acupressure is too—and you only need your fingers, rather than needles. And massaging the appropriate acupoints is a quick way of relieving the pain of a stress headache.

Press down firmly on the hollows in your temples, gradually increasing the pressure; hold for 20 seconds, then release. Then make small, circular, clockwise movements with your fingertips. Repeat as necessary. Or try using acupressure on the hollow at the top of your nose between your eyebrows or on the muscle between your thumb and first finger.

19 A problem shared

Sometimes, stress becomes so ingrained and part of your personality that stress-busting techniques just can't touch it. And that's when things become very serious indeed.

Subtly, insidiously, but surely, stress damages your health, let alone your ability to work. It plays a major role in a number of serious medical conditions, some of which can be fatal. So if you suffer from a high level of chronic stress it's imperative that you do something about it. Talk to your human resources manager, consult your doctor, and share your problem —it's the only way to stop doing yourself permanent damage.

20 Picture the scene

You can use visualization—conjuring up positive images—
in two ways: to prevent stress from developing in specific
situations, and to relieve it if it does. And the technique has
been medically proved to be a stress-buster.

As a preventive, rehearse all the possible scenarios for
a meeting beforehand, concentrating on positive images of
how you react to different situations. As a treatment, conjure
up images of places and
situations in which you've
felt truly relaxed—lying on
a beach, say—and use all
your senses to make the
situation as real as possible.
You'll soon feel your
worries drift away.

21 Map things out

Sometimes there's nothing more stressful than having to make a decision, especially when you just can't work out what to do for the best. That's when a spiderweb can take the stress out of making up your mind.

Write your main question inside a circle drawn on a piece of paper. Then draw branches off the circle, with each one listing a chain of the problem's various considerations and implications—use a different color for each branch. Mapping out the problem and associating its factors with colors involves both sides of your brain, and especially your creative centers, with the decision-making.

De-stress at home

After a hard day's work, your home should be
a comfort and a sanctuary. For sheer indulgence
in a calming environment, follow these tips to turn
your home into the perfect stress-free environment.

22 Feng shui your home

Life energy, or chi, doesn't just flow through the human body but through the atmosphere, too, according to feng shui practitioners. So if you feel stressed out at home it could be because the flow of chi is being blocked by your home's layout or decoration.

The best solution is to hire a feng shui practitioner. Otherwise, buy a book and give your living space a DIY overhaul: bear in mind that clutter, badly sharp-leaved plants all disrupt chi. And by the way, to show you really know what's what, pronounce it "fung shoy."

23 Paper therapy

You probably haven't made a paper airplane and tried to fly it since you were at school. If that's the case, you're missing out. These days, origami is used to help calm violent prison inmates, to reduce agitation in mental health patients, and to lower stress levels and build teamwork industry.

It's not surprising, really. Working through a series of delicate, precise paper folds not just demands but creates calm concentration—many devotees say that it's almost Zen-like. So buy a pattern book, switch off the TV, get some paper, and start folding. And why limit yourself to a plane?

24 Wrap yourself up

Sometimes the best way of reducing your stress levels is to be thoroughly indulgent and pamper yourself disgracefully. And one way to do it is to replace all your bed linen, towels, and wraps with Egyptian cotton.

It's strong, yet soft and sensuously silky. When it's next to your skin you feel as if you're being brushed by a million butterfly wings. When you get in at the end of a long, hard day, just throw on an Egyptian cotton wrap and relax into low-stress luxury. It's a little pricey, but treat yourself—you know you're worth it.

25 Flower power

There's no mystery, scientifically speaking, about why smells are so evocative: they are recognized and associated with specific feelings by the limbic system, the brain's seat of emotions. The trick is to pick a scent that corresponds with the emotion you'd like to feel.

For most people, the light, fresh, almost buttery fragrance of gardenia (Gardenia thunbergia) hits the right buttons for relaxation and contentment. It's a hardy shrub that's easy to grow indoors—it just needs light and warmth. And there's a bonus: since time immemorial, gardenias have been associated with love and romance. You never know!

26 Yogalates™

It's claimed to develop core strength, help tone muscles, increase flexibility, and reduce stress—and it's the new exercise buzzword. Yogalates™ was invented by Australian exercise guru Louise Solomon, who cherry-picked the best bits from yoga and Pilates.

The result is an exercise and stress-busting technique that you can learn in classes—or from books and videos—and then put into practice at home. The fusion between the breathing systems of yoga and Pilates is said to be particularly effective, so that you end up toned and fit with a sense of inner calm, relaxation, and health.

27 Sound bath de-stress

One way of fighting stress is to retreat to the comfort and security of your own private world. And taking a sound bath is an ideal way of doing it.

Simply get comfortable, close your eyes, and listen to music through a pair of headphones. Ideally, the music you choose should have a regular, slow beat, just like the pulsing of your mother's heart—the constant feature of your life in her womb. After about 20 minutes, your breathing will have become deeper and more regular, your heart rate will have reduced, and your brain will have started to produce serotonin, a feel-good chemical.

28 Relax into blue

I don't know why they call it the blues, because the fact is that the color blue improves your mood—and it de-stresses you, too. Blue's relaxing qualities were first proved scientifically as long ago as 1973, when researchers in America found that bathing subjects in red light for 30 minutes caused both the heart rate and blood pressure to rise, whereas blue light decreased them.

So if you feel stressed at home, your decor might be partly to blame. Consider replacing vivid, strident colors with relaxing pastels based on blue and start to sing a happier tune.

29 Climb into a bathtub

There's nothing better than a long soak in a hot tub. The heat relaxes tense, knotted muscles and eases tired joints, while the water provides comfort and support that maximizes the opportunity for quiet reflection.

And you can make the experience even more de-stressing by simply adding a few cups of Epsom salts (magnesium sulfate) to your bath—don't if you have high blood pressure or a heart condition. This naturally occurring mineral acts as a detox agent. To complete the effect, add some aromatic oil to the bath—or, better still, a handful of rose petals.

30 See the light

It's generally accepted that in some people a lack of natural light can lead to seasonal affective disorder (SAD), a form of depression. Less well known, though attested by a fair amount of research, is that artificial light, which has a reddish-yellow tinge, can also affect our emotional well-being.

There's a simple solution. Fit full-spectrum natural daylight bulbs in your home and experience the de-stressing benefits of daylight throughout the evening. You'll also find that the light they shed makes reading easier on the eyes and allows you to judge colors more accurately.

31 Aquarium de-stress

In Japan, watching jellyfish is all the rage; in Europe, children stare contentedly at goldfish bowls; and in America a survey showed that seven out of ten aquarium owners find that their fish act as stress-busters.

It's not clear why watching fish swim about should be so relaxing, but it certainly does the job. It's best if you choose fish that school, so that you can enjoy their balance and harmony as they dart and turn in mysterious unison. And if you don't find the idea a bit too kitsch, you could always buy a coffee-table aquarium.

32 Burst a bubble

When two New Jersey inventors came up with the idea of bubble wrap in 1957, they were trying to make plastic wallpaper. In fact, they'd invented one of the simplest and best stress-busters around.

The de-stressing benefits of popping bubble wrap have been demonstrated by psychologist Dr. Kathy M. Dillon, who says that the technique works because your hands tighten up when you're stressed and it relieves their tension. But that's to underestimate the sensual satisfaction you get from popping the bubbles. Others acknowledge this: Chase's Calendar of Events has named the last Monday in every January as Bubble Wrap Appreciation Day worldwide.

33 One thing at a time

One of America's National Mental Health Association's top stress-busting tips is to take one thing at a time. It's because stress can make it almost impossible to cope with a normal workload, even around the house, and your inability to get things done just makes you even more stressed.

The answer is to prioritize all your tasks and address them one by one. Don't get distracted by any other job: just keep going until you've finished it. Then you can relish the feeling of satisfaction at having checked a task off your to-do list and move on to the next one.

34 Fighting fit

One way of getting rid of the high levels of adrenaline that stress produces as part of the "fight or flight" reaction is to have a fight. Not a real fight, of course, but a simulated one —with a punch bag.

Just batter away at a punch bag, hitting as hard as you can, and within minutes you'll feel your tensions drain away as the adrenaline is used up. Don't forget, too, that boxing provides a very good workout, leaving you fitter and stronger. And to make the experience even better, you can always pretend that the punch bag's your boss.

35 Piece things together

You either love jigsaws or loathe them. But if you're one of those people whose eyes light up when they see a new puzzle, you're in luck—doing a jigsaw significantly lowers your stress levels.

It's probably because jigsaw aficionados become so absorbed in the puzzle they're doing that they just don't have any brain capacity left over for worrying. But a word of warning: make sure that you pack every single piece away securely when you finish a puzzle—you'll become very stressed indeed if a piece is missing next time you come to do it.

36 Praying for calm

People have known that prayer and meditation promote calm for centuries. But it's only been since the research of Dr. Andrew Newberg, of the University of Pennsylvania, in the 1990s that we've been able to prove it. He used newly developed imaging technologies to demonstrate that prayer directly affects the brain, increasing awareness and peacefulness, and boosting both the immune system and creativity. Now more than 60 U.S. medical schools are teaching courses on religious and spiritual issues.

So pray regularly to your god— or meditate if you'd prefer—and let the sweet, small voice of calm enter your soul.

37 Money talk

Financial worries are a major cause of stress—it's hard to relax when you're up to your ears in credit card bills and you just can't seem to make ends meet. But it's important to do something positive about your finances in order to stop your stress levels and your life getting out of control.

The first thing to do is to draw up a budget. List all your outgoings—be honest, all of them—and balance them against your income. Then decide which outgoings you're going to have to cut. It's hard, but it's necessary for your sanity.

38 Rock your troubles away

The image of granddad rocking back and forth contentedly in a rocking chair on the porch or in front of the fire is almost a stereotype. But like many stereotypes, it has a basis in fact—and scientific fact at that. Because a recent study at the University of Rochester Nursing School has shown that rocking reduces anxiety and tension in older people and eases emotional distress.

There seems no reason why it shouldn't have the same effect on everybody. So get yourself a rocking chair and try a regular rocking chair de-stress—about half-an-hour a day is said to do nicely.

39 Slow-burning sugars

It's all too easy to comfort eat when you're stressed: suddenly a slice of cake or a handful of cookies seem just too hard to resist. The reason is that the sugars these foods contain act as a pick-me-up, elevating blood sugar levels massively. Unfortunately, though, the sugar is soon burned off and blood levels plummet—and these rapid swings increase your levels of stress.

The answer is to eat complex carbohydrates such as cereals, rice, pasta, and bread. Their sugars break down slowly, over a long period, keeping sugar levels stable. So check out your fridge and throw temptation in the bin.

40 Spring clean

There's something strangely comforting about spring cleaning—and you don't even have to do it in the spring. Cleaning your house from top to bottom is almost ritualistic: it's as if it marks a turning point, a new beginning to your new low-stress life.

Set aside a weekend and go through your home, room by room. Be ruthless and throw away everything that you've been hoarding on the off chance it'll be useful. Tidy, organize, vacuum, dust, clean, and polish. By the end of the weekend, you'll be tired and relaxed and starting to enjoy the stress-free pleasures of your new-look home.

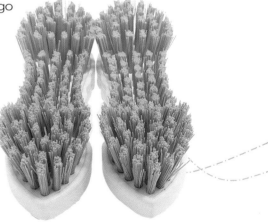

41 Regain control

Stress makes you dither about decisions and removes your ability to change situations that aren't to your liking. And feeling that you're just not in control of things is one of the most stress-making feelings of all. If you fit this bill there's only one thing to do: regain control.

The first thing to do is to run an audit of your life—your work, your home life, and your relationships. Write out a list of what you want to change and how you're going to carry out the change. Then take the hard decisions. Just do it.

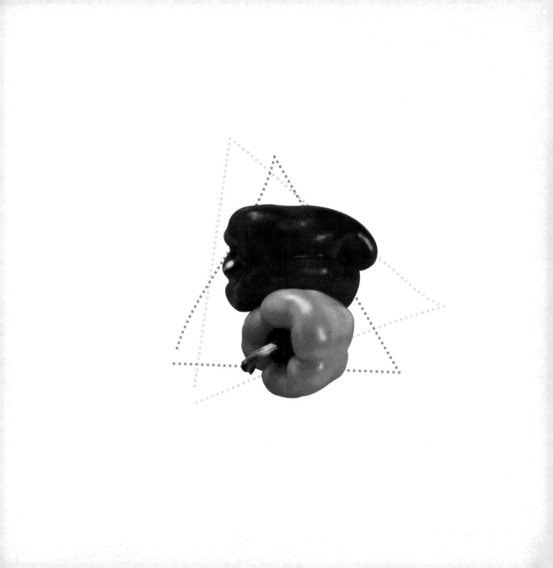

De-stress for health

From what you eat to how you exercise, your
lifestyle choices not only help keep the stress levels
down, they give you a healthy body too.

42 Five-minute de-stress

A recent Cornell University Wellness Program study established that just five minutes of exercise each day not only improved fitness levels but also had beneficial psychological effects. That's because regular exercise is a de-stresser.

You can pack a lot of effort into five minutes—take it gently at first, though—and you can certainly afford the time. Alternating standing squats and prone push-ups will work nearly every muscle in your body. Aim to work up to two sets of 20 repetitions of squats with two sets of 20 push-ups. After a few weeks of this you'll feel the benefit—in both relaxation and health.

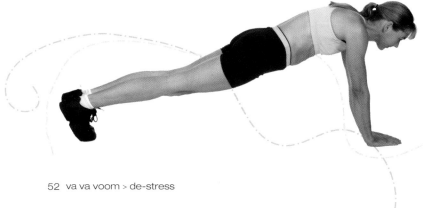

43 Move it!

Obesity looks as if it's on course to become one of the major killers of the 21st century. But being overweight isn't just extraordinarily unhealthy—it also causes physical and emotional stress.

The catch-22 is that stress hormones activate fat receptors deep in the abdomen—it's part of stress's classic "fight or flight" survival reaction. So the more you're stressed, the more fat you lay down, and the unhealthier and more stressed you become. There's only one way out of the vicious circle, and that's to combine weight-loss measures, such as exercise and a diet, with your stress-busting regime.

44 Stand tall

Stress affects your posture: you tend to slouch and hunch up your shoulders and keep your muscles tense. And that's a recipe for trouble in the neck, shoulder, and back.

It's simple to correct your posture and reduce the physical effects of stress. Stand in front of a mirror and look straight ahead with your chin in a neutral position and your neck in the midline. Push the crown of your head up, elongating your neck, then put your shoulders back—though not rigidly—and tuck your bottom in. Then walk away, maintaining the position. After a little practice, correct posture will become second nature.

45 Fish oil de-stress

There's plenty of evidence that the omega-3 fatty acids found in fish oil are good for your health—they increase the blood ratio of good cholesterol to bad cholesterol. But now studies are starting to indicate that they are also able to combat depression and stress.

So top up your omega-3 levels by eating several servings of oily fish each week—salmon, tuna, herring, sardines, and mackerel, for example. And if that seems a bit too fishy, you can always take a fish-oil capsule, available from health stores, or even try some of the omega-3 enriched eggs and bread that have recently come on the market.

46 No smoking

It's hardly a secret that cigarettes are extremely bad for your health. Even so, many people continue to smoke because they think they're helping relieve stress.

They couldn't be more wrong. Since the early 1970s, scientists have been puzzling over "Nesbitt's Paradox." The riddle was why people smoke to relax even though nicotine causes brain arousal in the short term; yet they also smoke to become more alert when ultimately nicotine depresses brain activity. Now it's known that nicotine withdrawal effects—between cigarettes—decrease alertness and increase stress. Smoking relieves these effects temporarily but increases stress overall. So give up!

47 Catch some rays

Sunbathing has had a bad press lately. And it's not surprising, because overexposure to the sun can cause skin cancer. But if you're sensible, take precautions, and don't overdo it, soaking up the sun's rays can be a great stress-buster.

So give it a try. You'll also be increasing your levels of vitamin D production, reducing your blood pressure, warding off the effects of seasonal affective disorder (SAD), a form of depression caused by a lack of ultra-violet radiation, and even combating some skin disorders. Sensible sunbathing is a recipe for good health and relaxation.

48 Alcohol de-stress

I know, I know. A few glasses of wine make you see the world through rose-tinted glasses and are even said to be good for your health. So why not? The trouble is that anything more than a few glasses has a different effect. Alcohol disrupts your appraisal of stress, so that you perceive it less if you're a little drunk beforehand, but you perceive it more if you become drunk afterwards. And that's just your perception of stress—not your stress levels themselves. So make sure you only drink alcohol in moderation: anything more is dangerous for your health and doesn't affect stress. Try other stress-busters instead.

49 Antioxidant de-stress

You can't open the papers these days without reading about antioxidants. They help destroy "free radicals"— that is, unbalanced molecules that lead to "oxidative stress"—which contribute to degenerative conditions such as atherosclerosis, heart disease, and stroke.

So it makes sense to boost your antioxidant intake and reduce your stress levels— as a bonus, antioxidants help keep your skin elastic and young-looking. Eat more berries, Brazil nuts, hazelnuts, chestnuts, raisins, black grapes, cherries, broccoli, spinach, carrots, tomatoes, prunes, peas, peppers, and sweet potatoes. You'll fight oxidative stress, feel healthier, and look better.

50 Boost your immune system

One of the more insidious effects of stress is that it depresses your immune system, making you more susceptible to viral infections, such as coughs and colds—which, in turn, increase your stress levels.

There are a number of ways in which you can avoid this extra stress by boosting your immune system. You could take a whole range of health supplements, of course. But just as good, and a lot more pleasurable, are two proven immune boosters:  chocolate and yogurt. With these, and a good night's sleep and some light exercise, you'll be fit to fight off both viruses and stress.

51 Sleep tight

Having trouble sleeping is one of the classic symptoms of stress. But sleeping problems increase your stress levels, because without sleep you just can't cope the next day and sleep becomes even more elusive. Yet a good night's sleep is vital to health.

In the long term, sleeping pills don't work and can be dangerous. Instead, just adjust your behavior. For example, stick to regular bedtimes and getting-up times, even at weekends. Don't drink alcohol or caffeine drinks or eat a heavy meal near bedtime. Just make sure you sleep tight and you'll minimize your stress.

52 Alexander technique

In 1879, F.M. Alexander, an Australian actor, found that he kept losing his voice on stage. Eventually, he discovered that at the root of his problem was the way he moved his head—and the Alexander Technique was born.

The Technique is a teaching process rather than a therapy. An Alexander teacher will diagnose your patterns of movement and posture and re-educate you into "patterns of good use" that become habitual with practice. Sign up for a course and you'll soon find that physical stresses become a thing of the past and your overall health and attitude to life has greatly improved.

53 A high-fiber diet

Irritable bowel syndrome sounds fairly unpleasant, and it is. Essentially, it's an abnormality in the function of the colon that can lead to spasms, cramps, and diarrhea—and it's exacerbated, if not caused, by stress. And, naturally, having IBS is stressful.

One solution is to incorporate dietary measures into your general stress-busting program. Change to a low-fat, high-fiber diet, with plenty of whole grain breads and cereals, pulses, fruits, beans, and vegetables. Eat smaller meal portions more often, too. That way you'll avoid stressful IBS, have a better balanced diet and guard against a number of intestinal problems.

54 Magnesium de-stress

Magnesium is often referred to as "the anti-stress mineral." This is because it acts like a physical tranquilizer, relaxing not only skeletal muscles but the muscles that line blood vessels and the digestive tract. It also plays a very important part in body chemistry.

Most people have lower magnesium levels than they should, especially because alcohol, caffeine drinks, sugar, and drinking soft water all leach it from our bodies. You can get round the problem and take advantage of magnesium's stress-busting properties by eating more nuts, seeds, dark green vegetables, legumes, and whole grain foods. Or, if you must, take a mineral supplement.

55 Hit the squash court

Ever wondered why so many business executives play games such as squash and racquetball? Partly to network, certainly, but also because hard physical effort relieves stress.

During a long, hardworking day, you experience continual, low-level "fight or flight" reactions that leave your body overloaded with adrenaline. If this isn't released, it can damage your cardiovascular system. But hard physical exercise—not too hard at first, unless you're already in peak condition—uses up the leftover adrenaline as well as any produced by the demands of the game. It's a triple whammy: you relieve stress, protect your cardiovascular system, and improve your fitness.

56 Slow down

It's not just mystic eastern healers who can learn how to control their pulse rates and blood pressure—we can all do it. And it's an important skill to acquire, both to relieve stress and to improve general health.

Try it yourself. Find your pulse and concentrate on slowing it: focus your mind and intone "slower," "slower," "slower." This works for many people, but if it doesn't or you want to learn more sophisticated techniques, visit a biofeedback clinic. As well as receiving tuition, you'll be connected to a variety of machines that give you a read-out of how well you're doing.

57 Stock up on spinach

The American Federal Drug Administration (FDA) approves only a few "health claims" for foods. But it has allowed: "foods that are good sources of potassium and low in sodium may reduce the risk of high blood pressure and stroke." It's because the balance between potassium and sodium controls the body's fluid levels, and so blood pressure— which stress increases.

Most people's standard diet doesn't contain enough potassium. But you can make up the difference if you eat plenty of oranges (and drink orange juice), bananas, potatoes, spinach, and beans. And look for products bearing the approved health claim.

58 Man's best friend

No, not the four-legged kind. It's a yoga position called "The dog" (Adho Mukha Svanasana)—and Harvard Medical School agrees that yoga reduces anxiety, blood pressure, and heart rate. And that relieves stress and boosts general health.

"The dog" energizes the body, slows the heart rate, and increases suppleness and strength. Get down on all fours with your toes behind your heels and your palms stretched out. Then come up on your toes and hands, raising your buttocks and lowering your head as your arms go out in front—you should look like an up-turned "V." It's hard at first, but it's worth it.

59 Identify the cause

Often the cause of stress is a deep-rooted anxiety or an emotional problem, and physical stress-busters won't really help. The answer is counseling—but not just any old type of counseling. The only one that has been shown to be effective against stress is cognitive behavioral therapy (CGT).

In CGT, the therapist tries to identify the root cause of your stress and alter your response to it, changing negative perceptions in a logical way. Behavioral techniques are also taught to change your expectations. It sounds complex, and can take some time, but it's effective. Give it a try.

60 Low salt de-stress

There's been considerable controversy in medical journals recently about whether eating too much salt increases blood pressure and so raises stress levels (though for people with certain conditions, salt restrictions are essential). At the moment, the balance of the argument seems to lie with those experts who say that it does. So just to be sure, it's a good idea to limit the amount of salt you eat. The worst culprits when it comes to salt content are processed foods, in which it's often hidden. Avoid them if you can, and resist the temptation to add table salt to your meals.

61 Feel the heat

According to health clinic owners, taking a sauna relieves stress, relaxes muscles, improves the circulation, and makes you feel great. They would say that, wouldn't they? But it seems that they may be right, according to an article in The American Journal of Medicine of February 2001.

Though larger-scale studies are needed, the article says, taking a sauna may lower blood pressure, improve lung function, and alleviate pain. And everyone's agreed that sauna bathing is extremely relaxing and pleasurable. So give it a try—but ask your doctor before you do, because there are risks if you have certain medical conditions.

De-stress for get-up-and-go

When you need that extra spurt of energy and want to make sure you're on top form, you need the following tips to make sure you can keep up—without getting stressed out.

62 Shoulder stand

Sarvangasana—it means "all parts pose"—or the "shoulder stand" is an ideal pick-me-up and tension-releaser that revitalizes the body—but take it very carefully at first.

Lie on the floor, legs together and palms down at your sides. Breathing in, push your hands down and raise your legs in a controlled way straight up and over your head and beyond to a 45° angle. Breathing out, support your lower back with your hands, push your back up and lift your legs. Now breathing slowly and deeply, press your chin to your throat, straighten your spine, make your legs vertical, and straighten your torso.

63 Forgive and forget

When you're stressed, insignificant slights become major insults. You try to blame everybody for your problems but yourself. And, self-pityingly, you tend to dwell on your setbacks and resent the people whom you believe caused them. The trouble is that doing this just uses up all your emotional energy and increases your stress levels.

So make a conscious effort to take responsibility for your own actions and understand and forgive the actions of others. That way you'll have more energy with which to meet the challenge of your own problems, resolve them effectively, and reduce your stress.

64 Breakfast boost

"Breakfast like a king; lunch like a prince; and dine like a pauper," the old saying goes. And, like many an old saying, there's a lot of truth in it. The fact is that if you skimp on breakfast—or, like many people, ignore it altogether—your energy resources just won't be sufficient to cope with the various demands of the morning. The result? You're stressed by lunchtime. So be sure you make time for breakfast—prepare everything the night before if that makes things easier. You'll avoid stress, feel in control of things, and discover a new sense of dynamism and drive.

65 Ginger up!

It's not surprising that people talk about "gingering you up," because that's just what ginger does. For centuries it's been known by herbalists all over the world for its energizing properties. But not so well-known is the fact that ginger also soothes you—as well as addressing a number of minor ailments, such as intestinal gripes.

And you can take ginger in a variety of ways. If you like Asian cuisine you'll already be familiar with it—otherwise you can drink ginger tea, or even refreshing, alcohol-free ginger beer and ginger ale. Let ginger fire up your life.

66 Positive thinking

It's hard to react to the challenges of everyday life with a sense of dynamism when you're stressed. One of the problems is that stress makes you feel that your get-up-and-go got up and left. And that perception can hit your self-esteem—hard.

But how can you restore your self-esteem and increase your energy levels? One way is to accentuate the positive. Make a list of all the good things about you and your life and concentrate on them. Consider how much they outweigh the negatives, then tell yourself that stress is only a learned choice and reject it.

67 Eat a banana

Have you ever wondered why tennis players almost inevitably eat a banana between sets? The easy answer is that a banana is packed with get-up-and-go, energy-rich carbohydrates—as well as fiber, vitamins, and minerals.

But there's another reason. Bananas contain three vital stress-busters: tryptophan, which is essential for the production of the feel-good brain chemical serotonin; vitamin B6, which is depleted by stress; and potassium, which is vital for brain function. So even if you're not up for a Grand Slam title, it's worth unzipping a banana whenever you want to maximize dynamism and reduce stress.

68 Transcendental de-stress

It's hard to forget—if you're a baby boomer, that is—the reaction when the Beatles introduced an Indian yogi called Maharishi Mahesh and his technique of Transcendental Meditation (TM) to the West in the 1960s. Even in those hippie days, there was considerable skepticism.

But in the decades since then, the cynics have been proved at least partly wrong. A considerable body of research has proved that regular TM can reduce stress and increase mental alertness. TM can be learnt from books and videos, but it's more effective to consult a teacher. Give it a try!

69 Have a laugh

Do you really think it's sensible that on February 2 each year, Groundhog Day, America convinces itself that a small animal can forecast the weather? And what's the idea with April Fool's Day and the annual cheese-rolling race in Gloucester, England? The answer is that they're all silly—and they cheer people up enormously.

Silly things make you laugh—a stress-buster in itself—and take your mind off your problems. They provide anything from minutes to hours of sheer escapism, during which your internal batteries can recharge themselves. So think of something very, very silly indeed—and go for it.

70 Dance the flamenco

This yoga-based exercise imitates one of the dance movements of the flamenco. It not only relieves tension in your chest, shoulders, and neck but leaves you feeling full of vitality.

Stand with your feet hip-width apart and arms by your sides, breathe in, and stand tall. Breathing out, move the backs of your hands in front of you until they touch in front of you, while simultaneously curving your torso and head toward your hands; hold for a few seconds. Then, breathing in, uncurl your torso and move your hands behind you until your palms are facing skyward, opening your chest and letting your neck fall back. Repeat three times.

71 Get munching

Psychologist Richard Thayer, of California State University, says that there are three ways of boosting your energy and so lowering tension: walking, listening to music, and . . . eating carrots.

Yes, yes. Bear with me. Energy levels often fall because blood sugar levels are low. You could eat some candy, but that would just make the levels surge and quickly fall again. But the sugar in a carrot is released into the bloodstream slowly, over a long period, and carrots are good for you, too. So put on your headphones, walk to the store, and buy some carrots now.

72 Mirror de-stress

Research has shown that when you frown, your immune system is weakened and that it perks up when you smile. It's because movement of the muscles involved triggers a brain reaction that responds pleasurably even when the pleasure isn't real.

So smiling is a stress-buster just by itself. But for some reason the effect is magnified if you smile into a mirror. Pull funny, smiling faces in a mirror for a few minutes and you'll be surprised how much more relaxed and energetic you feel. And a bonus is that people will respond to you more positively if you continue to smile.

73 Bach to rescue

Early last century, Dr. Edward Bach—say "Batch"—categorized 39 different negative emotions and discovered which flowers could help correct them by holding his hands over the flowers and using his intuition. Then he prepared an infusion of each flower in spring water, added a little brandy and Bach flower remedies were born. Many people swear by his Rescue Remedy, used to deal with moments of high stress and even panic and hysteria. But fewer know about Bach's Olive Remedy, which is specifically formulated to combat loss of vitality and exhaustion, or Wild Rose, which addresses apathy and resignation.

74 Rolfing de-stress

According to Dr. Ida Rolf, who developed the therapy called Rolfing in the 1950s in America, tension, anxiety, and stress are stored in the fascia—that's the network of thin, elastic connective tissue that enfolds every muscle and organ in the body. Rolfing practitioners release this tension and realign the body by means of a specialist form of massage that concentrates on the fascia rather than the muscles.

But Rolfing doesn't just relieve tension. Its adherents say that they feel strangely energized at the end of a session. So why not see if Rolfing works for you?

75 A game of solitaire

Sometimes all you need to do when you feel you're becoming stressed is to take a little time out—just long enough to disperse the adrenaline that's been building up, relax a little, let your subconscious work on what's been bugging you, and recharge your batteries.

 If you don't have a traditional solitaire board to hand, those kind computer programmers have given you an ideal way to do just that: a patience program called solitaire. Just play a few hands and you'll feel surprisingly refreshed, even if they don't come out. (Personally, I think the program cheats.) Just make sure the boss doesn't find out, or your stress levels may rise.

76 The sound of silence

Your mind buzzes when you're stressed, and you tend to fill up your time and your personal interactions with nervous, automatic chatter. When silent, thoughts chase each other through your brain, distracting you. And all this activity takes up valuable energy.

The solution is to discipline yourself. Try to develop the habit of counting to three inside your head before you speak. Listen to what's being said to you instead of thinking in advance about how you'll reply. Stop yourself if you find that your conversation is running away with itself. Conserve your energy and listen to the sound of your silence.

77 Nut de-stress

Eat a handful of nuts and you're packing your body with energy. But that's not the only benefit of eating them—so long as you choose the correct ones. To combine raising your energy levels with stress-busting make sure you pick peanuts, Brazil nuts, and almonds.

Peanuts contain biotin, which acts with the B vitamins to reduce the effect of stress hormones, while Brazil nuts contain thiamin (vitamin B1), which helps convert carbohydrates into energy at stressful times. And both almonds and Brazil nuts contain magnesium, which helps tense muscles to relax. Nuts to you if you don't take advantage.

78 Fall in love!

When Marlene Dietrich sang that she was falling in love again, she didn't sound too happy about it. That's a shame, because most people agree that there's simply nothing like falling in love to give you a spring in your step that just screams "energy."

So in the unlikely event that none of the stress-busters in this book work, you've still got one last chance of success: just fall in love. And if you've already got a partner, you could always try falling in love with him or her all over again. Enjoy!

79 Don't worry, be happy

The word "worry" is derived from the Old English term "wrygan," which also means "to strangle"—and that says it all. Insidiously, clawingly, worry gnaws away at your emotions.

But to stop worrying is easier said than done. The best solution is to take decisive action to sort out your problems. If that's not possible, try concentrating on the better things in life whenever you start worrying and conserve your energies.

80 Oxygen blast

It all started in Japan, with the realization that the oxygen concentration in the air we breathe is slowly reducing, especially in polluted cities. Soon "oxygen booths" and portable oxygen cylinders became features of Japanese life. Now the idea has spread to America, where you find "oxygen bars" in nightclubs and a range of oxygen sprays on sale.

It makes sense. Every cell in your body needs a continuous supply of oxygen in order to function, and even narrowly reduced oxygen levels can cause tiredness and stress. So try a blast of oxygen when you need to relax and re-energize.

81 Exercise with a purpose

It's generally accepted that exercise is one of the best stress-busters around, and that, paradoxically, it energizes you mentally and physically. But let's be honest: pounding a treadmill or swimming laps is often just plain boring.

That's why there's now a move toward putting the purpose back into exercise. If you tie exercise in with a meaningful, purposeful activity you're more likely to reap the benefits from your extra motivation. It could be as simple as biking to work, taking a brisk walk every day with your dog or building a stone wall round the yard. The choice is yours.

De-stress to feel good

If you just need something to make you smile or want a reminder of how good life can be, these tips will give you all the secrets of happy self-indulgence without the stress of guilt.

82 Vanilla scents

Maybe it's the childhood memories of vanilla in ice-creams and sweets, or vanilla's warm, soft, rich, heady scent or even its exotic origin as an orchid. Whatever the reason, vanilla's pungent fragrance has been proved to reduce stress and anxiety: in one study, cancer patients undergoing scans reported an incredible 63 percent reduction in their anxiety levels when exposed to it.

So relax into the beguiling scent of vanilla when you need to de-stress. Just put a few drops of vanilla onto a handkerchief and waft your cares away. But make sure it's pure vanilla essence—vanilla-based perfumes and oils aren't nearly as effective.

83 MBSR de-stress

Mindfulness-Based Stress Reduction (MBSR), a meditation technique, was first developed at the University of Massachusetts Stress Reduction Clinic in 1979. In the years since then, it's proved effective time and time again.

The technique, which is usually taught in a two-week course, involves learning first mindfulness—an acute but calming awareness of our inner feelings, our physical and sensory experiences and our reactions to different situations—and then mindful meditation, sometimes with physical stretches. Once mastered, MBSR is practiced daily, to reduce stress, increase vitality, and feel great—both about yourself and about your life.

84 Go on—giggle!

There are now around 1,000 of them worldwide, with 500-odd in India and around 200 in America, and they're the next big thing. What are they? Laughter clubs.

It makes good scientific sense. A study presented at the 2002 meeting of the U.S. Society for Neuroscience showed that even knowing days in advance that you'll be involved in a humorous event reduces levels of stress hormones and increases those of relaxation hormones. And the changes last long after the event itself. So join your local club now. If you can't find one, promise yourself a comedy video next weekend—or just laugh out loud.

85 Melissa essential oil

According to a 2002 paper in
The Journal of Clinical Psychiatry,
aromatherapy treatment with
Melissa essential oil is an
effective way of reducing
agitation in Alzheimer's patients.
The oil comes from Melissa
officinalis, also known as lemon
balm. And if it combats agitation,
it combats stress.

You can use it in several different
ways: in a vaporizer; diluted with
carrier oil for a massage; or inhale
a few drops from a tissue. In the words
of Gerard, the 16th-century herbalist,
you'll find that it "comforteth the hart
and driveth away all sadnesse."

86 Chocolate indulgence

It's possible that Daniele Piomelli has one of the best jobs in the world. He heads a team at San Diego's Neurosciences Institute that has spent several years trying to find out why eating chocolate makes you feel so good.

It must be a hard job, though, because chocolate contains some 300 chemical compounds, among them stimulants, amphetamine-like compounds, and neurotransmitters. One neurotransmitter, anandamide, which also occurs naturally in the brain, is thought to work in a similar way to the main ingredient in cannabis. But does this all matter? Chocolate de-stresses. So don't feel guilty— have some now.

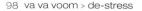

87 Go it alone

Information overload is one of the curses of the modern age. We're bombarded with e-mails, phone calls, and 24-hour news on the TV. All of which causes stress.

Peter Suedfeld, Professor of Psychiatry at the University of British Columbia, has researched the stress levels of Arctic explorers and scientists, and says that solitude is the answer to overload stress: "It restores your ability to think clearly, be creative and maintain an emotional calm." So search out quiet places—it's worth a try.

88 Shiatsu therapy

Shiatsu is a Japanese therapy that combines acupressure to manipulate the body's energy flows and sophisticated massage techniques. It's claimed to regulate hormone levels, improve the circulation, and help eliminate waste products.

But don't worry about that. The main point is that a shiatsu session releases muscle tension and relaxes you. A shiatsu massage will reduce stress, and leave you feeling wonderful.

89 Pamper yourself

When you're stressed you need a little tender loving care. You need something that makes you feel good, look good, and relaxes you. In short, you need to be pampered.

   And there's an easy way to get what you want. Have your hair done, or go for a facial, a manicure, or a pedicure. If you've time enough and the money, spend a day in a health farm, taking in as many treatments—beauty or otherwise—as you can. Relax in the luxury of having someone else make you feel good. You'll come out looking and feeling like a million dollars.

90 Four-legged de-stress

In 1999, Dr. Karen Allen, of the State University of New York at Buffalo, found 48 stockbrokers who were taking medication to combat high blood pressure—it probably wasn't too hard —and gave half of them a cat or a dog. Guess what? The pets proved more effective stress-relievers than medication. In fact, many in the medication-only group ending up buying a pet.

It's because pets accept you as you are and give unconditional love and companionship, soothing you by their very presence. So if it's practicable, get a pet. It's not a hard trade to call, even for a stockbroker!

91 Relax by candlelight

It's often hard to find time for the finer things in life when you're stressed out. You're so busy worrying about your problems that there just doesn't seem to be enough time to let go and relax.

That's why it's important to schedule time for yourself—time in which you can force yourself to forget your problems and just enjoy the moment. How about a candlelit dinner? All you need is a relaxing ambience, some wine, some good food, some mood music, and your favorite person. A bit tacky? Don't be cynical—it'll do you no end of good.

92 Gone fishing

Well it doesn't have to be fishing. In this context, "fishing" is a catchall word that stands for any activity you please. Just so long as it's calm and solitary, you really enjoy it, find it endlessly absorbing, and you can't be disturbed.

Doing an activity in which you can lose yourself can put the active, worrying part of your mind in neutral, allowing your subconscious brain to organize your mental filing cabinets and work out what you really think. So whether your equivalent is playing with model railways or painting watercolors, just do it. And have a whale of a time.

93 Take a step back

Just say "no." It sounds one of the easiest stress-busters of all, but in fact it's one of the hardest. The trouble is that when you're stressed there's a terrible temptation to take on too much—perpetual motion allows you to avoid your own problems. But it just increases your stress levels.

So make a decision to step back and say "no." Then you'll have more time to reflect quietly on what's causing your stress and what you can do about it to make you feel good again. And you'll have time to start putting the stress-busting techniques in this book into practice.

94 Go for a swim

All exercise is good for stress relief, but swimming is particularly good. It's not just because doing some lengths in the pool works out a whole range of muscles, while the support of the water rules out most strains, sprains, and impact injuries. The fact is that swimming is a sensual and invigorating pleasure.

It may be the physical sensation as the water rushes over your skin, smoothing and polishing your worries away. Or it could be a resonance from the safe, warm, comforting fluid of your mother's womb. Either way, swimming de-stresses you and makes you feel great.

95 Jump into the shower

When you step into a shower, you're getting the benefit of three different stress-busters at the same time—and you feel refreshed and invigorated.

First, the pummeling effect of jets of warm water—especially those from a power shower—massages the tension out of your muscles. Second, when the water and heat are your only sensory inputs you can more easily take the opportunity to visualize the stresses of the day pouring off you along with the water. Third, the rushing water releases bracing, health-giving negative ions—charged particles—just like those produced by a desk ionizer. Just taking a bath is short-changing yourself.

96 Do a good deed

Australians are notoriously relaxed, laid-back people—think of Crocodile Dundee. And it just may be because Australia has a "Good Deed Day" on August 3 each year.

The fact is that doing someone a good turn doesn't just make you feel virtuous—almost righteous—and therefore good in yourself, but increases your self-esteem. In your own estimation you go up a peg or two, and for a while you elevate yourself above your day-to-day cares and worries. So donate to your favorite charity or give a stranger a helping hand and help yourself as well as others.

97 Whistle while you work

A miner's life isn't an easy one—and perhaps that's why the seven dwarves whistled as they worked. Because whistling cheers you up and reduces stress levels at the same time.

In order to whistle you need to take regular breaths through the nose, and exhale in a controlled way through pursed lips. That makes it similar to breathing exercises.

98 Spice things up

If you love chili, curry and other hot, spicy foods, you're in for a treat. You can indulge to your heart's content, safe in the knowledge that foods that take the roof of your mouth off actually lower your stress levels.

It's partly because strong taste sensations activate brain centers that override those dealing with other emotions. And at the same time, chemicals in ingredients such as chilies have been shown to trigger the release of feel-good endorphins in the brain. So there's a simple message: spice up your meals, chill—or even chili—out and feel great.

99 The benefits of baroque

Everyone knows that music can change your mood, but how do you know which type of music is most effective at relaxing you and making you feel good? Gangsta rap? Probably not. Country and Western? Maybe. In fact, countless studies have given us the answer—classical baroque music.

Baroque music is by composers such as Handel, Bach, Vivaldi, and Corelli, generally paced at around 60 beats a minute. Its beat and its intricate structures have been shown to produce more alpha brainwaves, which denote calmness, in both sides of the brain. Try it—you may never play those heavy metal CDs again.

100 At one with nature

Remember the last time you stood by a tumbling waterfall, or listened to the waves crashing on a distant beach? Watched as a butterfly struggled out of its pupa to take glorious flight for just a few hours, or contemplated the splendor of tropical fish?

Nature is so elemental that it puts you in your place. It's impossible to contemplate nature's wonders without feeling humble, yet at one with the world. And the realization of the insignificance of your problems breeds a sense of calm.

100 At one with nature

Remember the last time you stood by a tumbling waterfall, or listened to the waves crashing on a distant beach? Watched as a butterfly struggled out of its pupa to take glorious flight for just a few hours, or contemplated the splendor of tropical fish?

Nature is so elemental that it puts you in your place. It's impossible to contemplate nature's wonders without feeling humble, yet at one with the world. And the realization of the insignificance of your problems breeds a sense of calm.

99 The benefits of baroque

Everyone knows that music can change your mood, but how do you know which type of music is most effective at relaxing you and making you feel good? Gangsta rap? Probably not. Country and Western? Maybe. In fact, countless studies have given us the answer—classical baroque music.

Baroque music is by composers such as Handel, Bach, Vivaldi, and Corelli, generally paced at around 60 beats a minute. Its beat and its intricate structures have been shown to produce more alpha brainwaves, which denote calmness, in both sides of the brain. Try it—you may never play those heavy metal CDs again.

101 Adaptogen de-stress

Until the 1990s, adaptogens were one of the hidden secrets of Soviet science. They're plants that have broad-spectrum healing properties: and, specifically, it's claimed that they increase energy, improve alertness, promote restful sleep, and reduce stress levels.

The first adaptogens to become available worldwide were Chinese and Siberian ginseng. These didn't work for everybody, but another plant is now said to do just that. It's Rhodiola rosea, also known as Russian rosea, golden root, and Arctic root. It's available from most health food shops or the Internet, and if it does half what it's claimed to do it's worth trying.

Acknowledgments

Without the calming, de-stressing qualities of Nigel, Tom, and Cath Morgan, this book would never have been written. Thanks.